A FINE ROMANCE

& FOUR OTHER SONGS

ARRANGED BY DAVID NIELD

BOOK 3

ovello

Music of the sort collected in this book is immediately likeable, and it seems to transcend fashion: there is rarely any objection that it is out of date or inaccessible. David Nield, a teacher and choir director of long experience and immense understanding (he taught me!) has achieved here the feat of choosing good music and making sure that his arrangement keeps the spirit of the original solo in choral form without making it difficult to sing.

One or two things will help make an effective performance. With young singers, a mature bass may be added to the bottom part, because that helps to keep everyone in tune. Or the bass may be doubled with an instrument. A light kit drum part will help keep the beat steady and add colour. There is no rule that close harmony always has to be unaccompanied, so other instruments may be added. This style of music is best presented without copies, if only because that is often the only way of making the singers look up at their audience. In any case, the rhythms of this style of music are often obscured by notation, and we can remember them more easily by ear. Choreography will often make a performance far more effective, and the singers themselves will usually be ready to offer their own suggestions for movement If the singers are putting everything into the performance, the listeners are far more likely to enjoy themselves too.

RALPH ALLWOOD

Cover designed by Michael Bell Design.

NOV955075
ISBN 1-84609-165-9

Published in Great Britain by Novello Publishing Limited.

HEAD OFFICE
8/9 Frith Street, London W1D 3JB, England
Telephone: +44 (0)20 7434 0066
Fax: +44 (0)20 7287 6329

SALES & HIRE
Music Sales Limited
Newmarket Road, Bury St Edmunds, Suffolk IP33 3YB, England
Telephone: +44 (0)1284 702600
Fax: +44 (0)1284 768301

www.chesternovello.com
e-mail: music@musicsales.co.uk

Also in this series:
BOOK 1: SMOKE GETS IN YOUR EYES NOV955053
BOOK 2: ANYTHING GOES NOV955064

The way you look tonight

Dorothy Fields

Jerome Kern
arr. DAVID NIELD

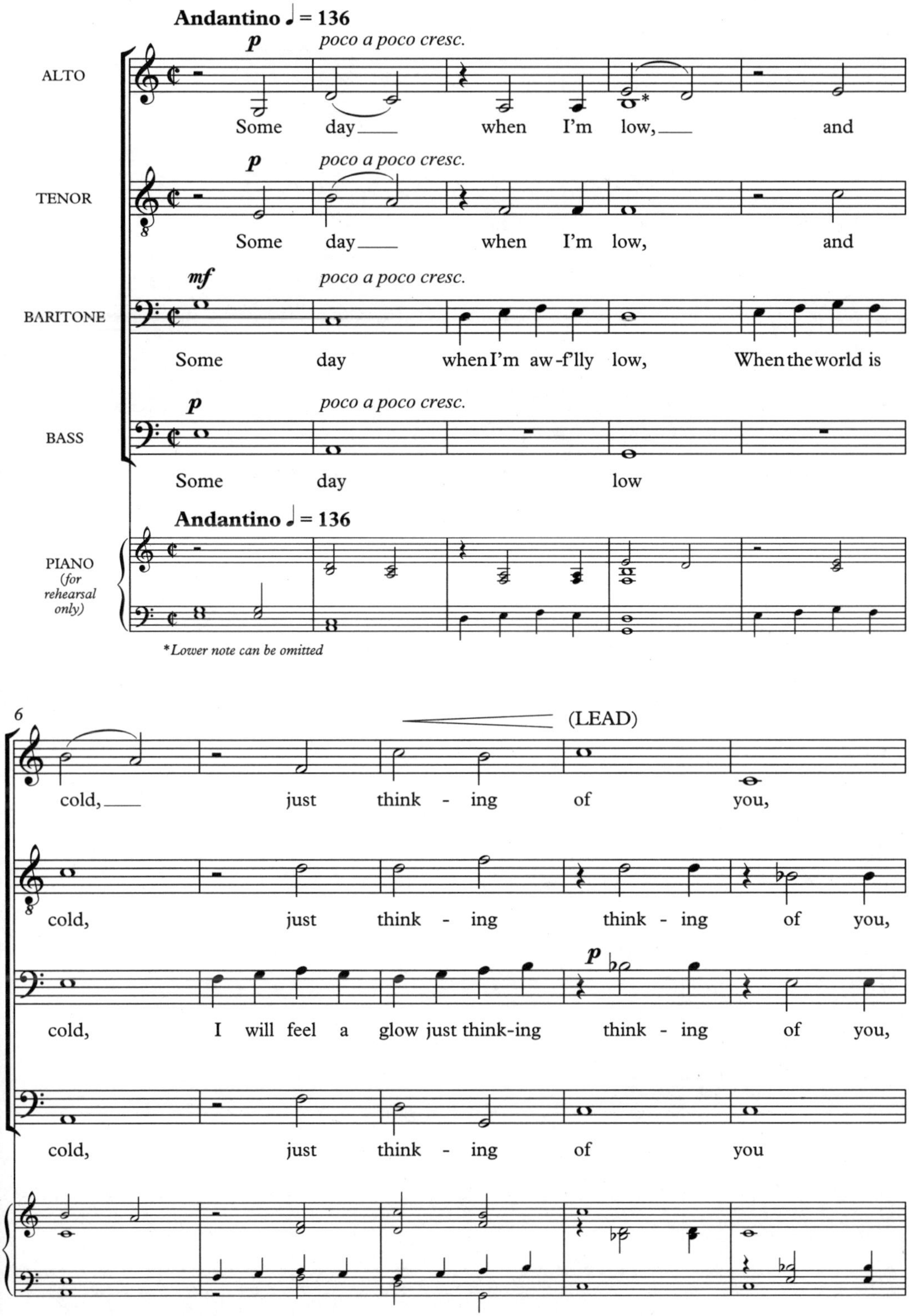

Andantino ♩ = 136

ALTO — *p* *poco a poco cresc.*
Some day when I'm low, and

TENOR — *p* *poco a poco cresc.*
Some day when I'm low, and

BARITONE — *mf* *poco a poco cresc.*
Some day when I'm aw-f'lly low, When the world is

BASS — *p* *poco a poco cresc.*
Some day low

Andantino ♩ = 136

PIANO (*for rehearsal only*)

**Lower note can be omitted*

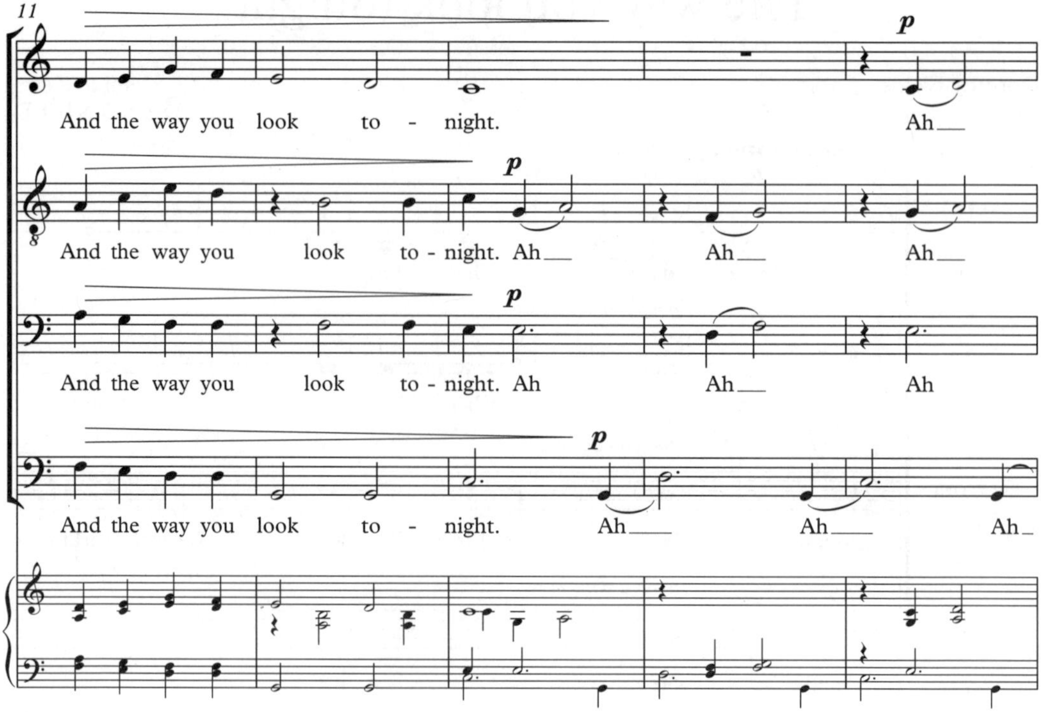

11
p
And the way you look to - night.
Ah
p
And the way you look to - night. Ah
Ah
Ah
p
And the way you look to - night. Ah
Ah
Ah
p
And the way you look to - night.
Ah
Ah
Ah

16
Oh, but you're love - ly, love - ly, smile so warm,
Oh, but you're love - ly, love - ly, smile so warm,
(LEAD)
Oh, but you're love - - ly, with your smile so warm,
Love - - ly, warm,

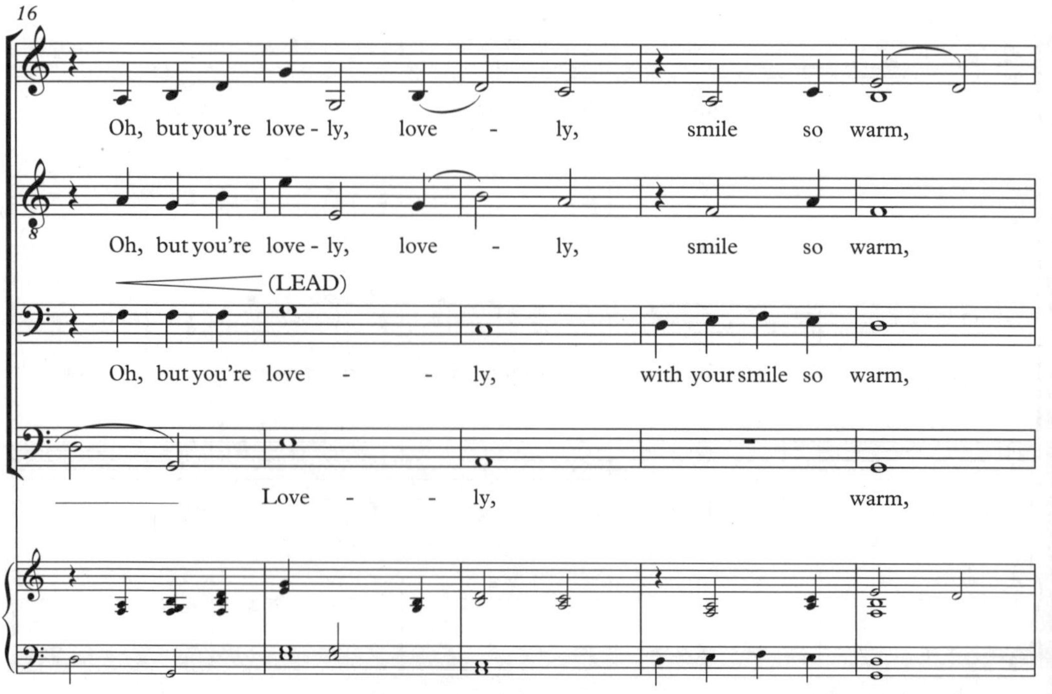

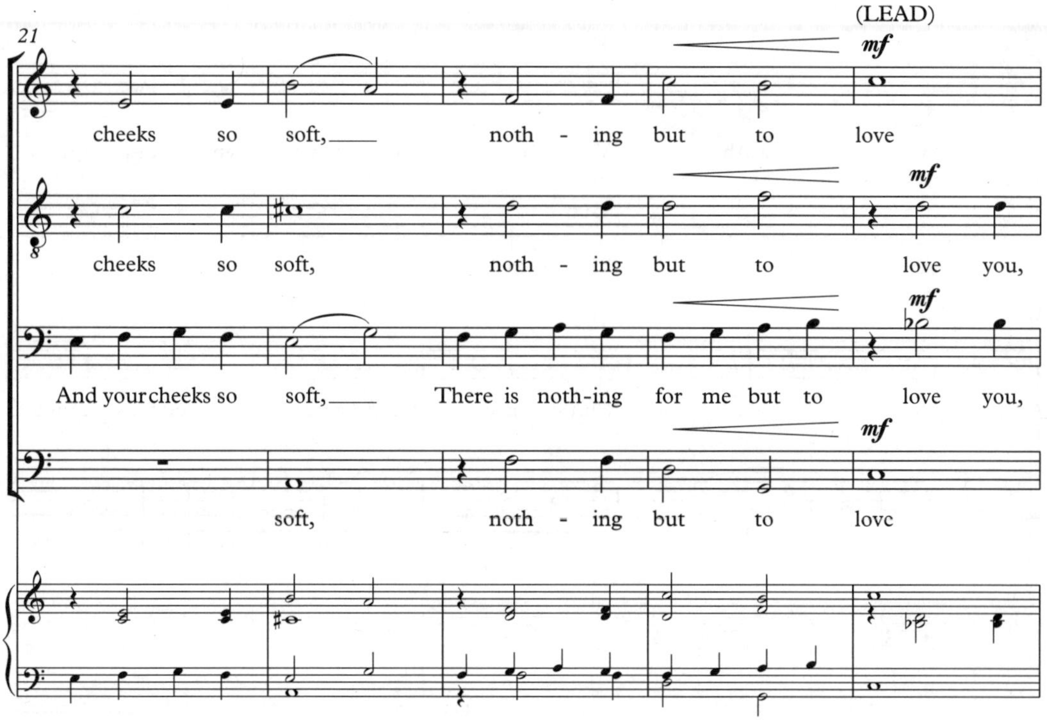

21
(LEAD)
mf
cheeks so soft, noth - ing but to love
mf
cheeks so soft, noth - ing but to love you,
mf
And your cheeks so soft, There is noth-ing for me but to love you,
mf
soft, noth - ing but to lovc

26
you, And the way you look to - night.
mp
love you, And the way you look to - night. Ah Ah
mp
love you, And the way you look to - night. Ah Ah
mp
you, And the way you look to - night. Ah Ah

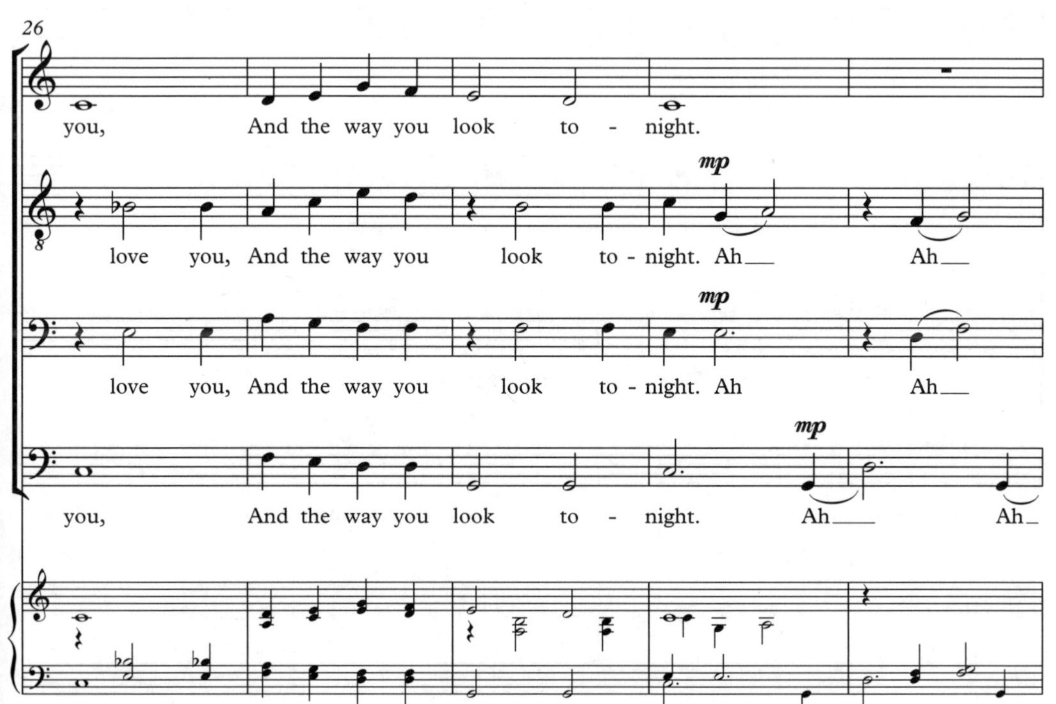

31

p

Ah — Ah — With each word, your ten-der-ness grows, —

Ah — Ah — With each word your ten-der-ness grows, —

Ah Ah With each word your ten-der-ness grows, —

— Ah — Ah — your ten-der-ness grows, —

36

— Tear-ing my fear — a - part, —

— Tear-ing my fear — a - part, —

— Tear-ing my fear, — Tear ing — my fear a - part, —

mf

— Tear-ing my fear, tear-ing my fear, — my fear a -

41

dim.

And that laugh that wrin-kles your nose__ Touch-es my

dim.

And that laugh_ that_ wrin-kles your nose__ Touch-es my

dim.

And_ that_ laugh that wrin - kles,___ wrin-kles your nose___

dim.

-part, that laugh that wrin - kles,___ wrin-kles your nose___

46

mf

fool - ish heart.___ Love - - ly,

mf

fool - ish heart.___ Love - - - -

mf

__Touch-es my fool-ish, my fool-ish heart.__ Love -

mf

__Touch-es my fool-ish, my fool-ish heart.__ Love -

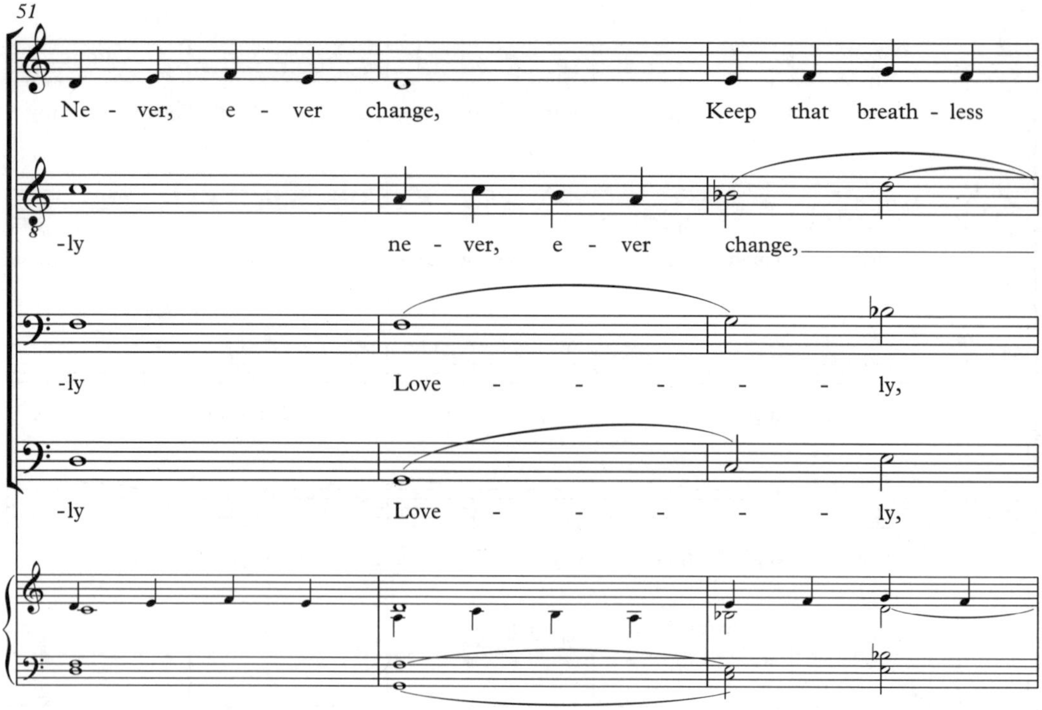

51

Ne - ver, e - ver change, Keep that breath - less

-ly ne - ver, e - ver change,

-ly Love - - - - - ly,

-ly Love - - - - - ly,

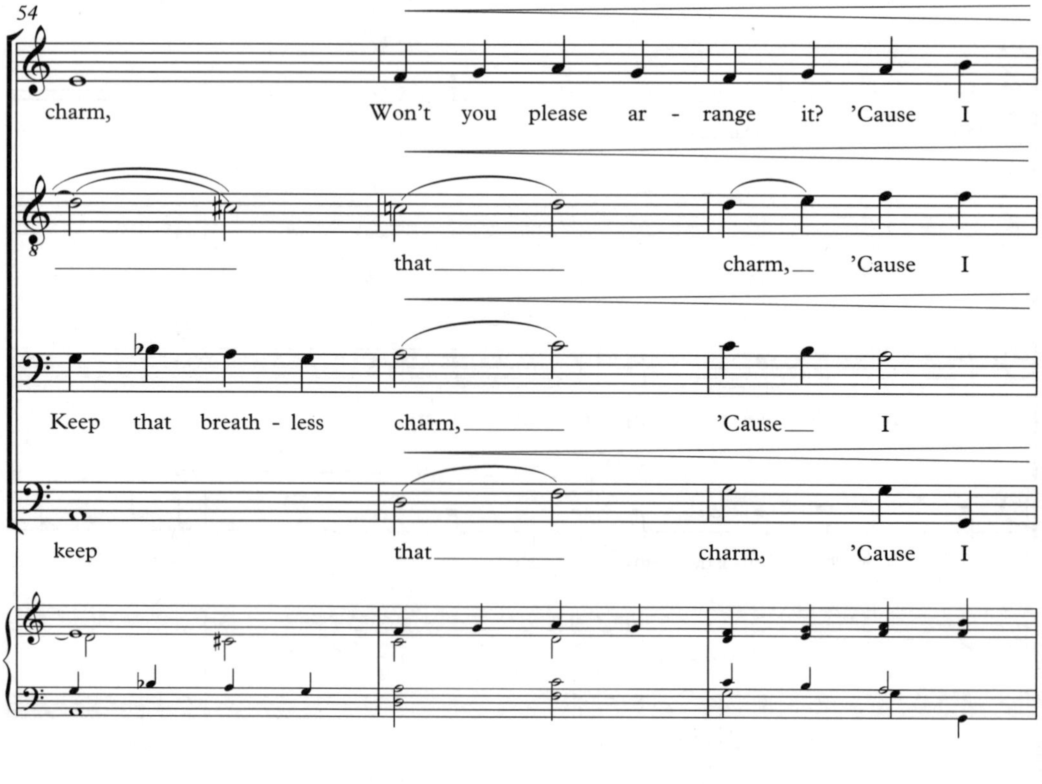

54

charm, Won't you please ar - range it? 'Cause I

that charm, 'Cause I

Keep that breath - less charm, 'Cause I

keep that charm, 'Cause I

57

f p

love you, Just the way you

f p

love you, I love___ you Just the way you

f p

love you, I love___ you Just the way you

f p

love you,___ Just way you

60

pp

look to - night, Ah___

pp

look___ to - night, Ah___ Ah___

pp

look to - night, Ah Ah

pp

look to - night, Ah___ Ah___

63

rit.

Ah___ Ah___ just the way you

Ah___ Ah___ just the way you

Ah___ just the way you

___ Ah___ Ah just the way you

rit.

66

look to - night, you look to - night___

look___ to - night, you look to night.

look to - night, you look to - night.

look to look to - night.

A Fine Romance

Dorothy Fields

Jerome Kern
arr. DAVID NIELD

10

ro-mance, my friend, this is! We should be like a cou-ple of hot to-
ro-mance! I'll take jel-lo! You're calm-er than the seals in the Arc-tic

ro-mance, my friend this is! ah
ro-mance! I'll take jel-lo! ah

ro-mance, my friend this is! ah
ro-mance! I'll take jel-lo! ah

doo wah doo wah doo wah

15

p

-ma-toes, ah mashed po-
o-cean, ah ...press e-

ah to-ma-toes, ah mashed po-
Arc-tic-o-cean, ah ...press e-

mf

ah to-ma-toes, But you're as cold as yes-ter-day's mashed po-ta-
Arc-tic-o-cean, At least they flap their fins to ex-press e-mo-

doo doo doo doo wah doo doo wah ah mashed po-
doo doo doo doo wah doo doo wah ah ...press e-

20

mf

- ta - toes, A fine ro - mance, you won't nes - tle, A
- mo - tion! A fine ro - mance, with no quar - rels, With

- ta - toes, A fine ro - mance You won't nes - tle, A
- mo - tion! A fine ro - mance with no quar - rels, A

p

- toes, A fine ro - mance, ro - mance, You won't nes - tle A
- tion! A fine ro - mance, ro - mance, with no quar - rels, A

- ta - toes, lah lah lah lah di lah lah lah lah di
- mo - tion! lah lah lah lah di lah lah lah lah di

25

fine ro - mance, you won't wres - tle! I might as well play
no in - sults and all mor - als! I've ne - ver mussed the

mf

a fine ro - mance you won't wres - tle! I might as well play
no in - sults and all mor - als! I've ne - ver mussed the

mf

a fine ro - mance you won't wres - tle! I might as well play
no in - sults and all mor - als! I've ne - ver mussed the

mf

lah lah lah lah lah lah lah lah, I might as well play
lah lah lah lah lah lah lah lah, I've ne - ver mussed the

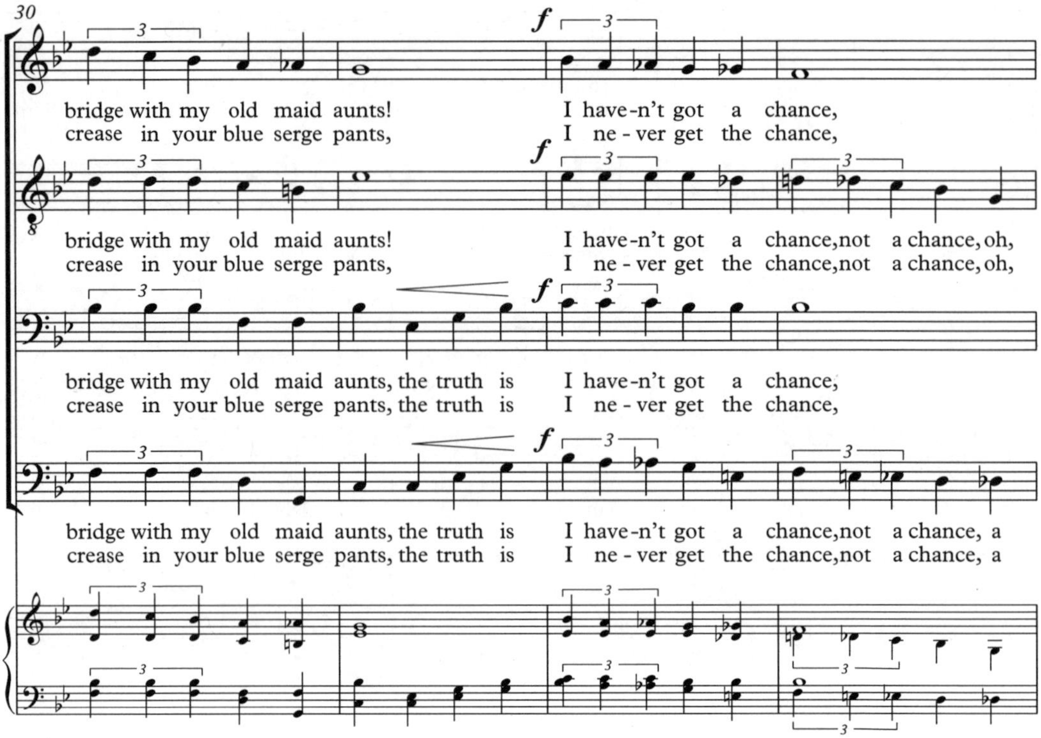

30

f

bridge with my old maid aunts! I have-n't got a chance,
crease in your blue serge pants, I ne - ver get the chance,

bridge with my old maid aunts! I have-n't got a chance, not a chance, oh,
crease in your blue serge pants, I ne - ver get the chance, not a chance, oh,

bridge with my old maid aunts, the truth is I have-n't got a chance,
crease in your blue serge pants, the truth is I ne - ver get the chance,

bridge with my old maid aunts, the truth is I have-n't got a chance, not a chance, a
crease in your blue serge pants, the truth is I ne - ver get the chance, not a chance, a

34

1.

p

this is a fine ro-mance! a fine ro- mance a fine ro-mance. A
this is a fine ro-mance!

this is a fine ro-mance! a fine ro- mance a fine ro-mance.
this is a fine ro-mance!

no chance, a fine ro- mance a fine ro-mance.
no chance,

fine ro - mance! A fine ro - mance. Ah
fine ro - mance!

1.

39

2. p

-mance, a fine ro - mance a fine ro-mance

-mance, a fine ro - mance a fine ro-mance

-mance, a fine ro - mance a fine ro-mance

-mance, a fine ro - mance, ah A

43

p sim

A fine ro - mance, with no kiss - es! A fine ro -
A fine ro - mance, my dear duch-ess! Two old

A fine ro - mance, with no kiss - es! A fine ro -
A fine ro - mance, my dear duch - ess! Two old

A fine ro - mance, with no kiss - es! A fine
A fine ro - mance, my dear duch - ess! Two old

fine ro - mance, with no kiss - es! A fine ro -
fine ro - mance, my dear duch- ess! Two old

48

p

-mance my friend this is! Ah
fo - gies who need crutch-es! Ah

mf 3

-mance my friend this is! We two should be like clams in a dish of
fo - gies who need crutch-es! True love should have the thrills that a heal-thy

mf 3

ro-mance, my friend, this is! We two should be like clams in a dish of
fo - gies who need crutch-es! True love should have the thrills that a heal-thy

mf 3

-mance my friend this is! We two should be like clams in a dish of
fo - gies who need crutch - es! True love should have the thrills that a heal-thy

3

3

53

mf 3 p

should be like clams in a dish of chow - - - - -
should have the thrills of a heal-thy crime

p

chow - der, chow - der, ah
crime has, ah ah

mf 3

chow - der, But we just fizz like parts of a Seid-litz
crime has! We don't have half the thrills that the 'March of

p

chow - der, Chow - der, ah
crime has! ah ah

3

3

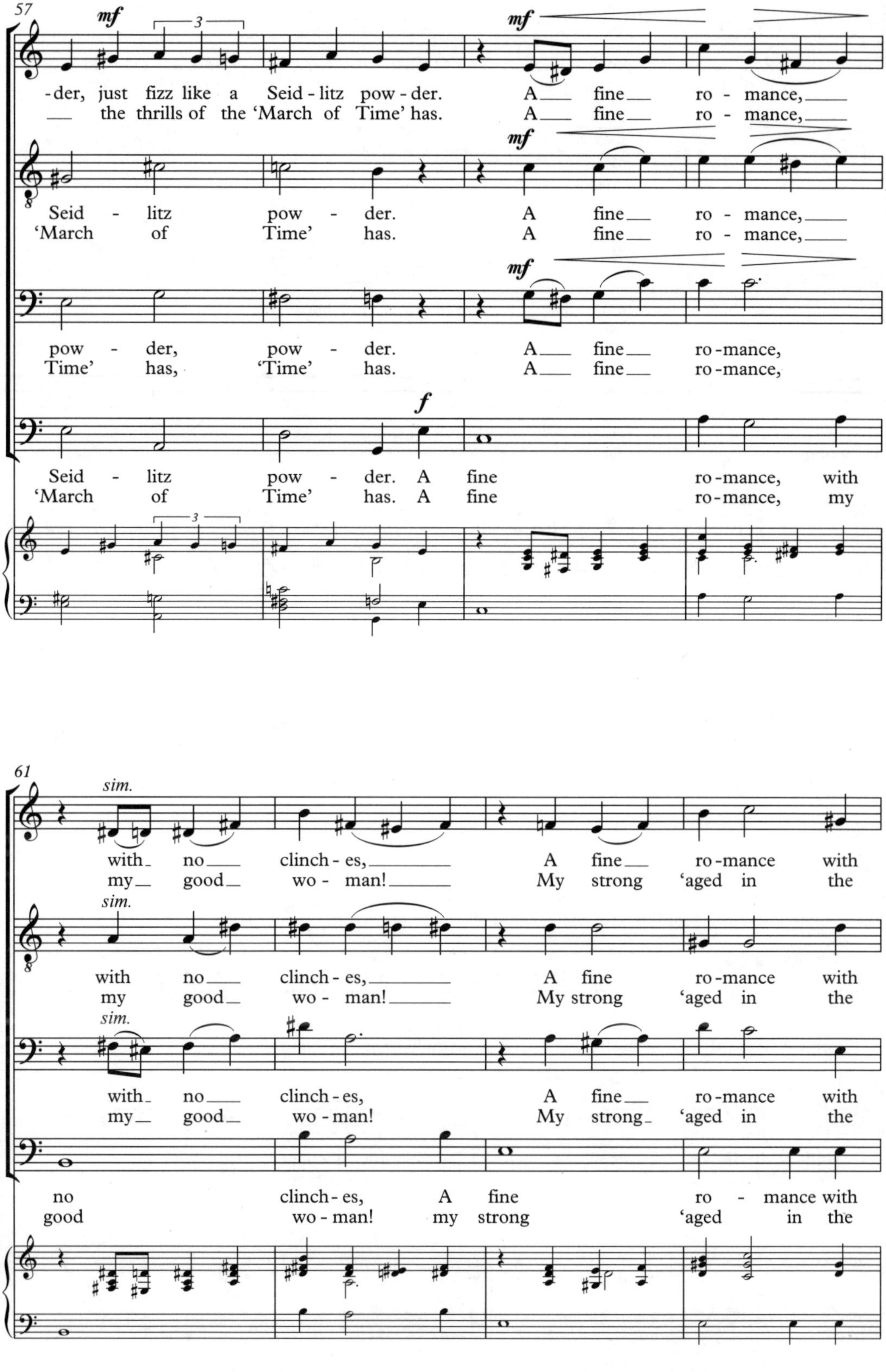

57

mf *mf*

-der, just fizz like a Seid-litz pow-der. A fine ro-mance,
the thrills of the 'March of Time' has. A fine ro-mance,

mf

Seid-litz pow-der. A fine ro-mance,
'March of Time' has. A fine ro-mance,

mf

pow-der, pow-der. A fine ro-mance,
Time' has, 'Time' has. A fine ro-mance,

f

Seid-litz pow-der. A fine ro-mance, with
'March of Time' has. A fine ro-mance, my

65
f
no pinch - es You're just as hard to land as the 'Ile de
wood' wo - man! You ne - ver give the or-chids I send a
no pinch - es You're just as hard to land as the 'Ile de
cast wo - man! You ne - ver give the or-chids I send a
no pinch - es You're just as hard to land to
wood' wo - man! You ne - ver give the or - chids, the
no pinch - es You're just as hard to land, to
wood' wo - man! You ne - ver give the or - chids,
3
69
1.
f
p
France', I have-n't got a chance, this is a fine ro-mance! a fine
glance, no, you like cac-tus plants,
France', I have-n't got a chance, this is a fine ro-mance! a fine
glance, no,you like cac-tus plants,
land as the 'Ile de France' I have-n't got a chance, fine ro-mance! a fine
or-chids I send a glance, no,you like cac-tus plants,
land as the 'Ile de France' I have-n't got a chance, fine ro-mance! a
or-chids I send a glance, no,you like cac-tus plants,

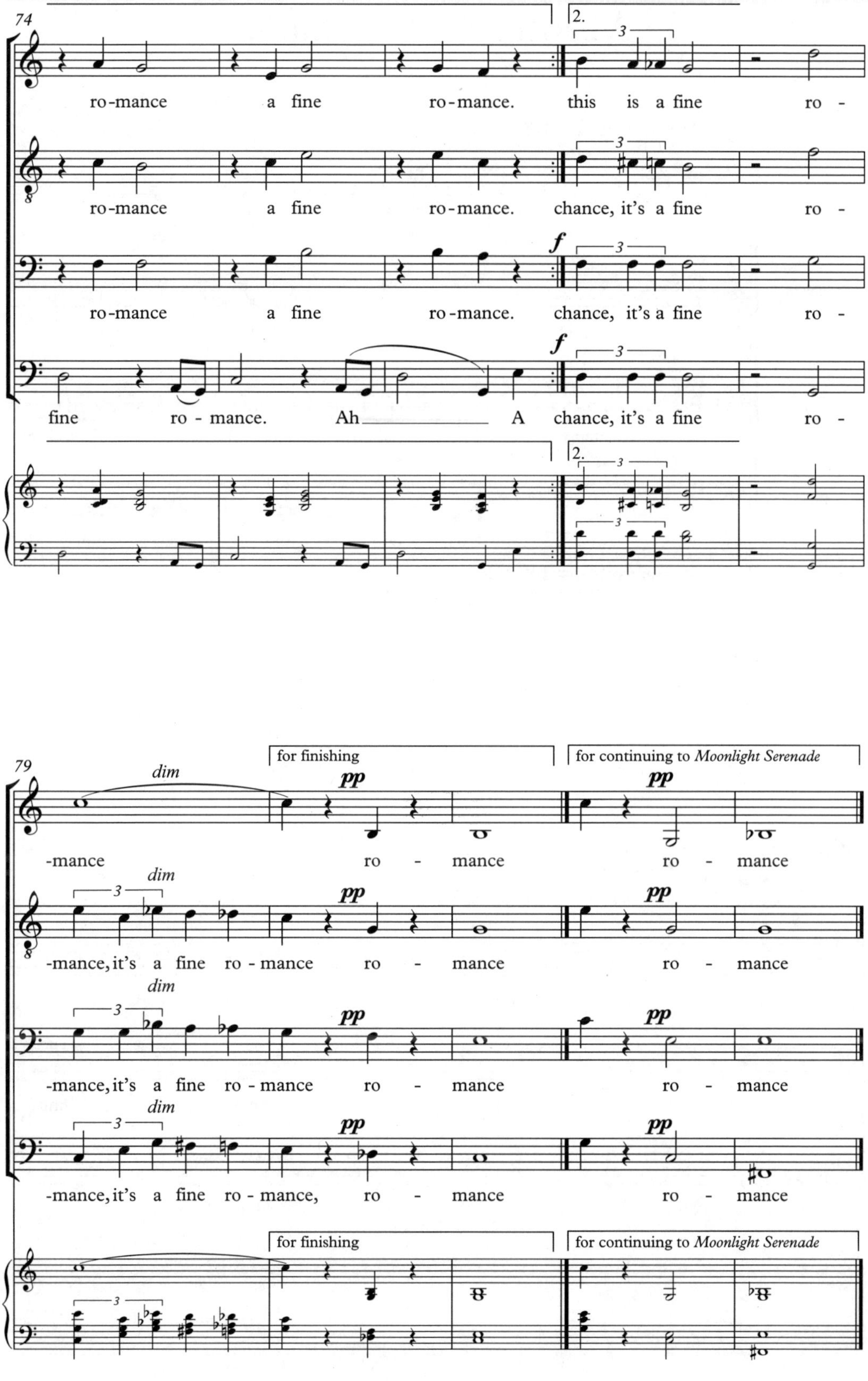

79

for finishing | for continuing to *Moonlight Serenade*

dim pp pp

-mance ro - mance ro - mance

dim pp pp

-mance, it's a fine ro - mance ro - mance ro - mance

dim pp pp

-mance, it's a fine ro - mance ro - mance ro - mance

dim pp pp

-mance, it's a fine ro - mance, ro - mance ro - mance

for finishing | for continuing to *Moonlight Serenade*

Moonlight Serenade

Mitchell Parish

Glenn Miller
arr. DAVID NIELD

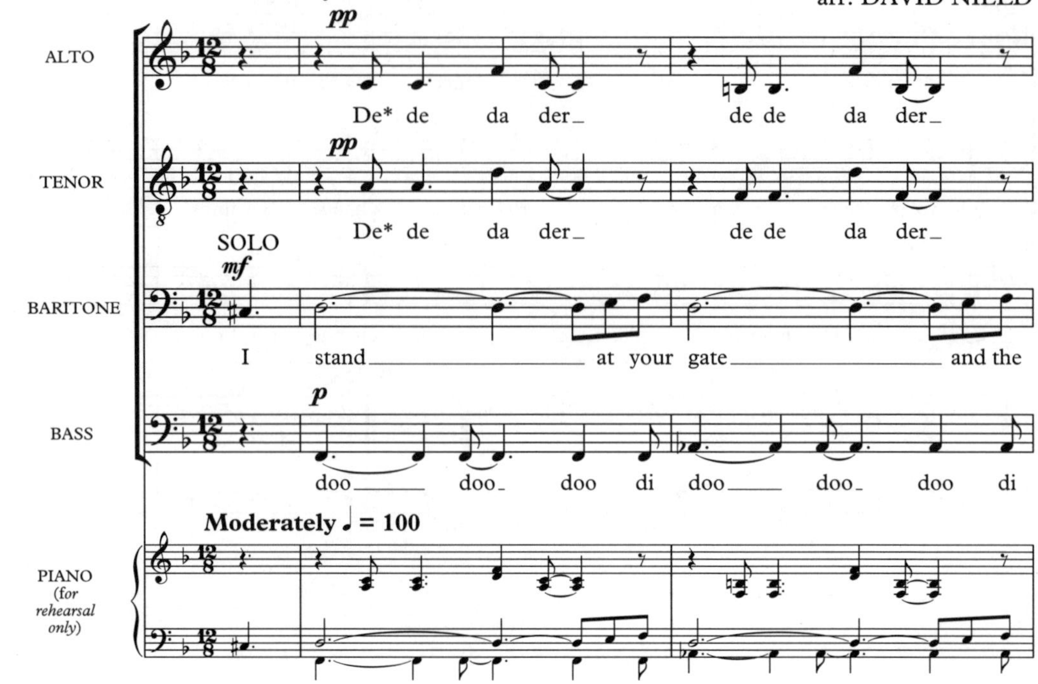

Moderately ♩ = 100

ALTO *pp*
De* de da der_ de de da der_

TENOR *pp*
De* de da der_ de de da der_

BARITONE SOLO *mf*
I stand at your gate and the

BASS *p*
doo doo_ doo di doo doo_ doo di

Moderately ♩ = 100

PIANO (*for rehearsal only*)

**'de' as in 'the'*

6

p

de de da der de de da der June night, the

p

de de da der de de da der June night, the

wait for the touch of your hand in the June night, the

doo wah doo wah doo wah doo wah June night and the

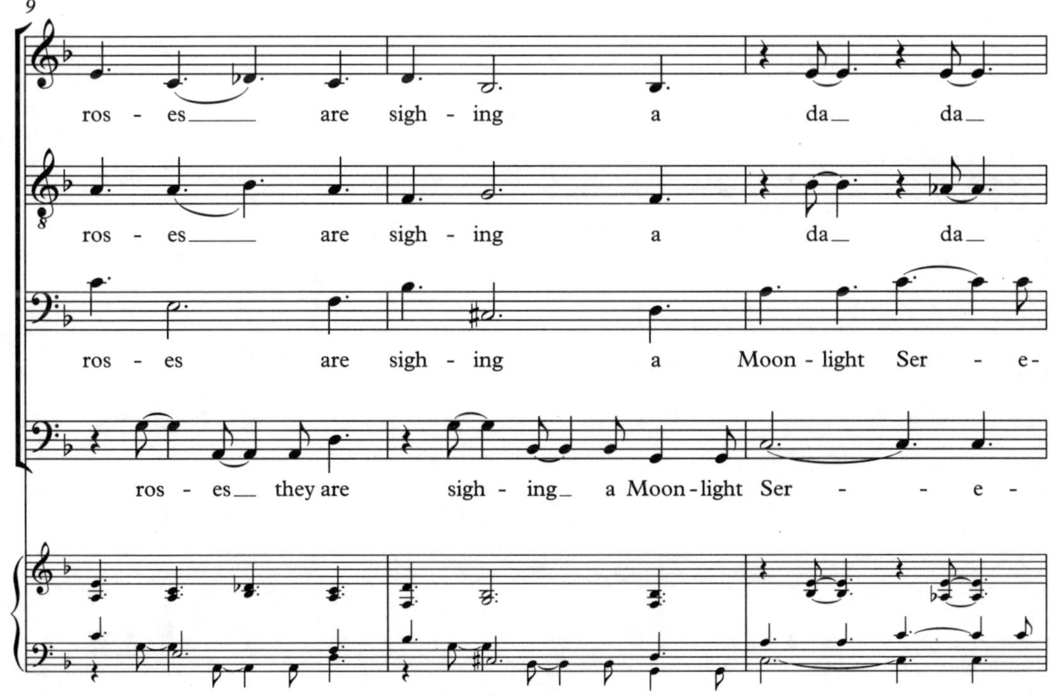

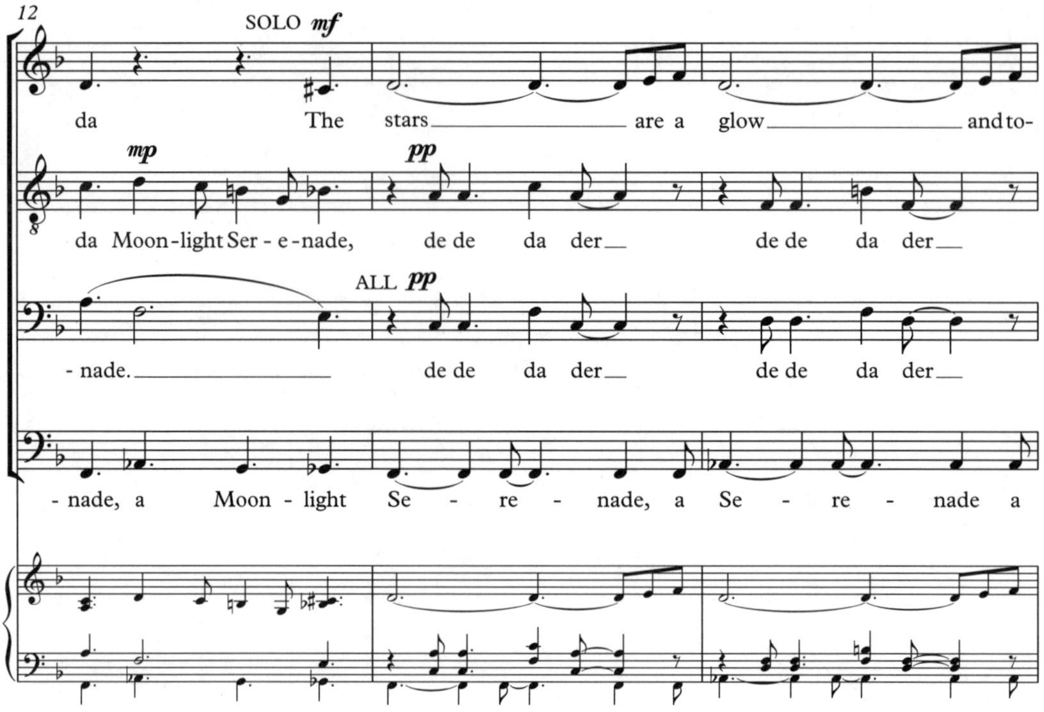

12
SOLO mf
da The stars are a glow and to-
mp pp
da Moon-light Ser - e - nade, de de da der de de da der
ALL pp
- nade. de de da der de de da der
- nade, a Moon - light Se - re - nade, a Se - re - nade a

15
-night how their light sets me dream - ing, My love, do you
de de da der me dream - ing, ah de de da der
de de da der me dream - ing, ah de de da der
Se - re - nade. I'm dream - ing a Se - re- nade a

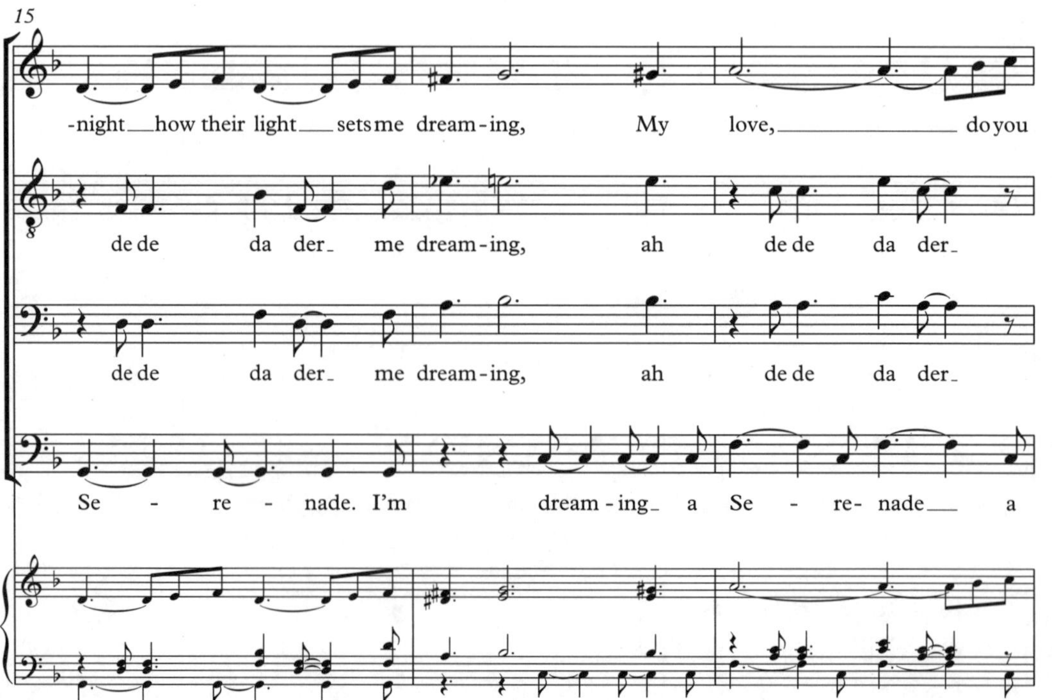

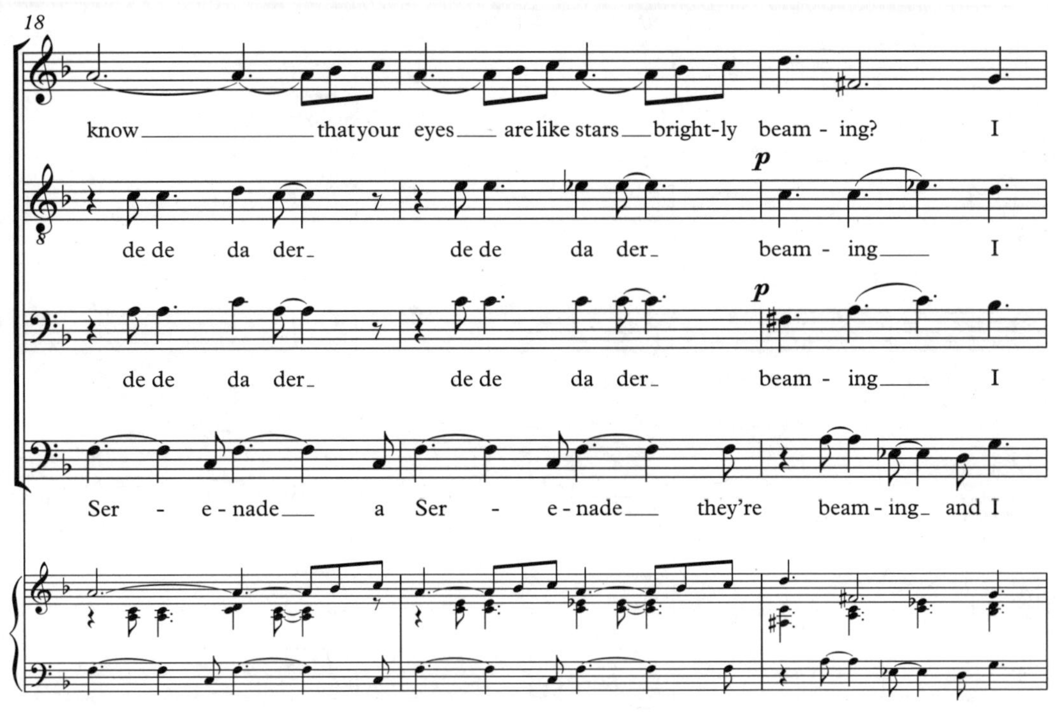
18
know that your eyes are like stars bright-ly beam - ing? I
p
de de da der de de da der beam - ing I
p
de de da der de de da der beam - ing I
Ser - e - nade a Ser - e - nade they're beam - ing and I

21
bring you and sing you a Moon - light Ser - e -
bring you and sing you a da da
bring you and sing you a da da
bring you and sing you I sing a Moon - light

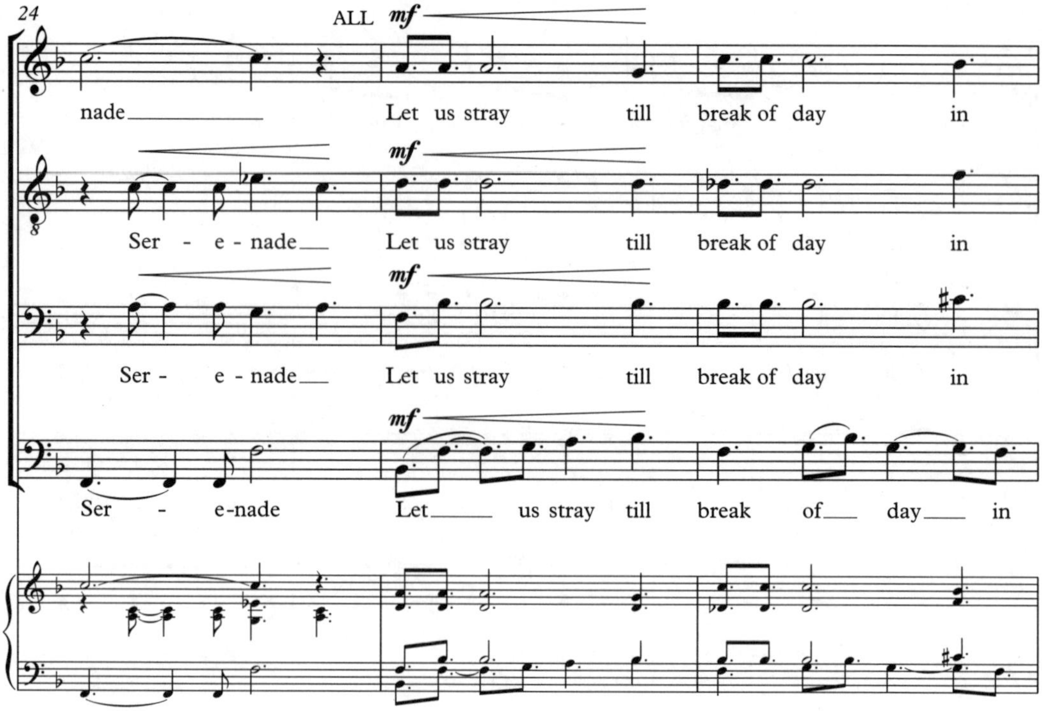

24
ALL mf
nade Let us stray till break of day in
mf
Ser - e - nade Let us stray till break of day in
mf
Ser - e - nade Let us stray till break of day in
mf
Ser - e-nade Let us stray till break of day in

27
love's val - ley of dreams, Just you and I, a
love's val - ley of dreams, Just you and I, a
love's val - ley of dreams, Just you and I, just you and I,
love's val - ley of dreams Just you, you and I

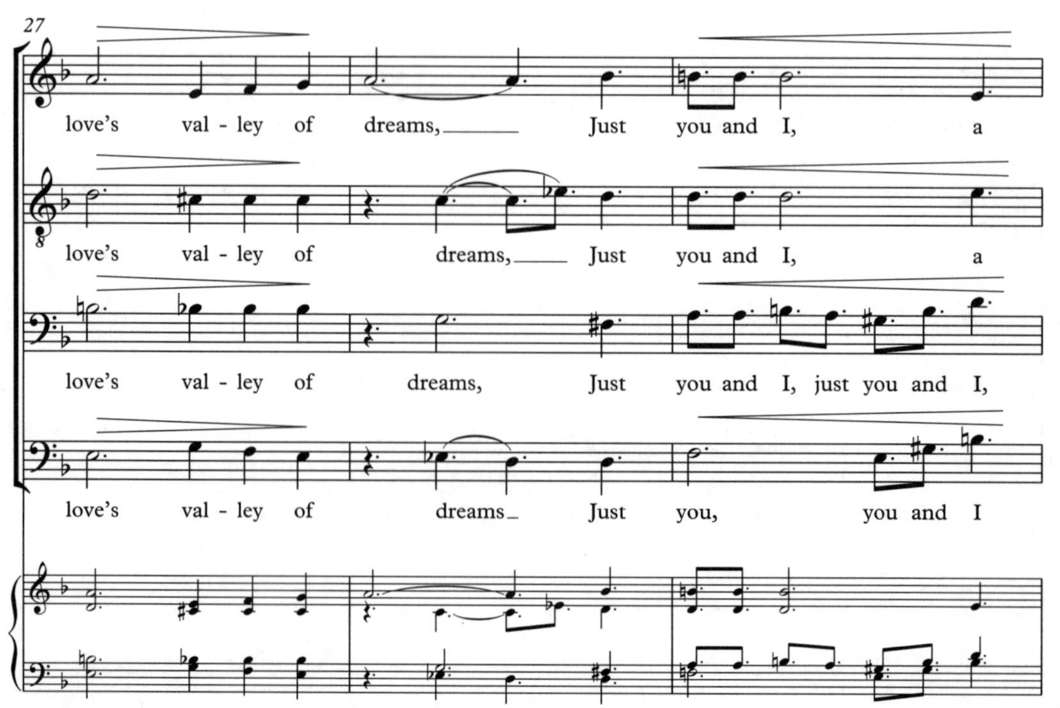

30 *f*

sum-mer sky, a heav - en - ly breeze kiss - ing the trees.

f

sum-mer sky, a heav - en - ly breeze kiss - ing the trees,

f

sum-mer sky, a heav - en - ly breeze kiss - ing the trees,

f *mf*

sum-mer sky, a heav - en - ly breeze kiss - ing the trees. So

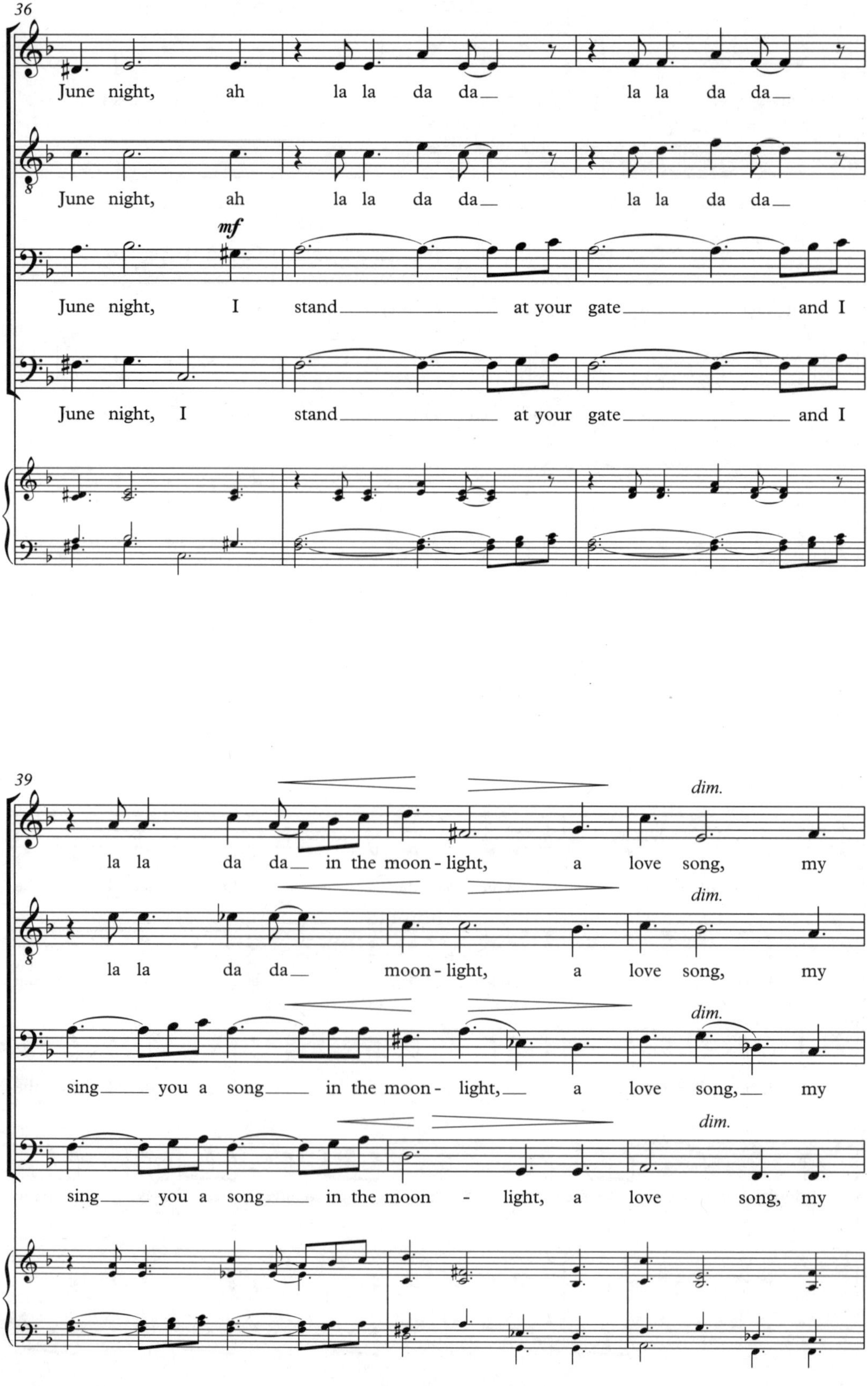

39

dim.

la la da da in the moon-light, a love song, my

dim.

la la da da moon-light, a love song, my

dim.

sing you a song in the moon- light, a love song, my

dim.

sing you a song in the moon - light, a love song, my

if finishing

42 rit. Slow

p *pp*

dar - ling, a Moon - light Ser - e - nade, Ser - e - nade.

p *pp*

dar - ling, a Moon - light Ser - e - nade, Ser - e - nade.

p *pp*

dar - ling, a Moon - light Ser - e - nade, Ser - e - nade.

p *pp*

dar - ling, a Moon - light Ser - e - nade, Ser - e - nade.

if finishing

rit. Slow

if continuing to *This can't be love* to bar 4

45 Slow Fast (♩ = 220)

pp *p*

-nade, Ser - e - nade. pa pa

pp *p*

-nade, Ser - e - nade. pa pa

pp *p*

-nade, Ser - e - nade. pa pa

pp *mf* SOLO

-nade, Ser - e - nade. This can't be

pp *p*

-nade, Ser - e - nade. la la

if continuing to *This can't be love* to bar 4

Slow Fast (♩ = 220)

This can't be love

Lorenz Hart

Richard Rodgers
arr. DAVID NIELD

Fast ♩ = 220

ALTO — *mf* This can't be love *p* pa pa pa pa

TENOR — *mf* This can't be love *p* pa pa pa pa

BARITONE — *mf* This can't be love *p* pa pa pa pa

SOLO *mf* This can't be love be - cause I

BASS — *mf* This can't be love *p* la la la

PIANO (*for rehearsal only*)

5

pa pa pa pa pa pa pa pa

pa pa pa pa pa pa pa pa

pa pa pa pa pa pa pa pa

feel so well, no sobs, no sor - rows, no

la la la la la la la la

9
p
I feel no sobs or sighs pa pa pa pa
p
I feel no sobs or sighs pa pa pa pa
p
I feel no sobs or sighs pa pa pa pa
sighs; This can't be love, I get no
la la la la la la la la
13
mf
pa pa pa My head is not in the skies, no lies!
mf
pa pa pa My head is not in the skies, no lies!
mf
pa pa pa My head is not in the skies, no lies!
mf
diz - zy spell. My head is not in the skies,
la la la la My head is not in the skies, no lies!

18
SOLO mf
My heart does not stand still, just hear it beat!
p
ah
mf
just hear it
ba ba
p
ah
ba ba
— my heart does not stand still, just hear it beat!
p
ah
la la
22
This is too sweet to be love
p cresc.
beat
bah da bah da bah da bah da
cresc.
ba ba bah da bah da bah da bah da
cresc.
ba ba bah da bah da bah da bah da
This is too sweet to be love.
cresc.
la la bah da bah da bah da bah da

27 ALL
mf
oh, this can't be love 'cos I feel so well I
mf
oh, this can't be love 'cos I feel so well I
ALL mf
This can't be love be - cause I feel so well; But still I
mf
oh, this can't be love 'cos I feel so

31
love to look to look in your eyes, yes right in your eyes.
love to look to look in your eyes, yes right in your eyes.
love to look in your eyes.
well to look, to look in your eyes.

35
f
pa da pa da pow Hey! pa da pa da pow Wow!
f
pa da pa da pow Hey! pa da pa da pow Wow!
f
pa da pa da pow Hey! pa da pa da pow Wow!
ff
This can't be love be-cause I feel so well, no

39
pa da pa da pow pa da pa da pow pa da pa da pa da pa da pa
pa da pa da pow pa da pa da pow pa da pa da pa da pa da pa
pa da pa da pow pa da pa da pow pa da pa da pa da pa da pa
sobs, no sor - rows or sighs;

43
bi doo bi doo boo Hey! bi doo bi doo boo Yeah!
bi doo bi doo boo Hey! bi doo bi doo boo Yeah!
bi doo bi doo boo Hey! bi doo bi doo boo Yeah!
This can't be love, I get no diz - zy spell. My

47
bi doo bi doo bi doo bi doo doo boo pa da pa da my heart does
mf
bi doo bi doo bi doo bi doo doo boo pa da pa da pa da my heart does
mf
bi doo bi doo bi doo bi doo doo boo pa da pa da pa da my heart does
mf
head is not in the skies. pa da my heart does

51
not stand still, just hear it beat! This is too
not stand still stand di doo di doo doo doo
not does not stand di doo di doo doo doo
not does not stand still doo di doo doo doo

55
sweet to be love.
doo doo doo doo doo doo doo doo doo doo doo doo doo doo doo doo doo doo doo doo
doo doo doo doo doo doo doo doo doo doo doo doo doo doo doo doo doo doo doo doo
doo doo doo doo doo doo doo doo doo doo doo doo doo doo doo doo doo doo doo doo

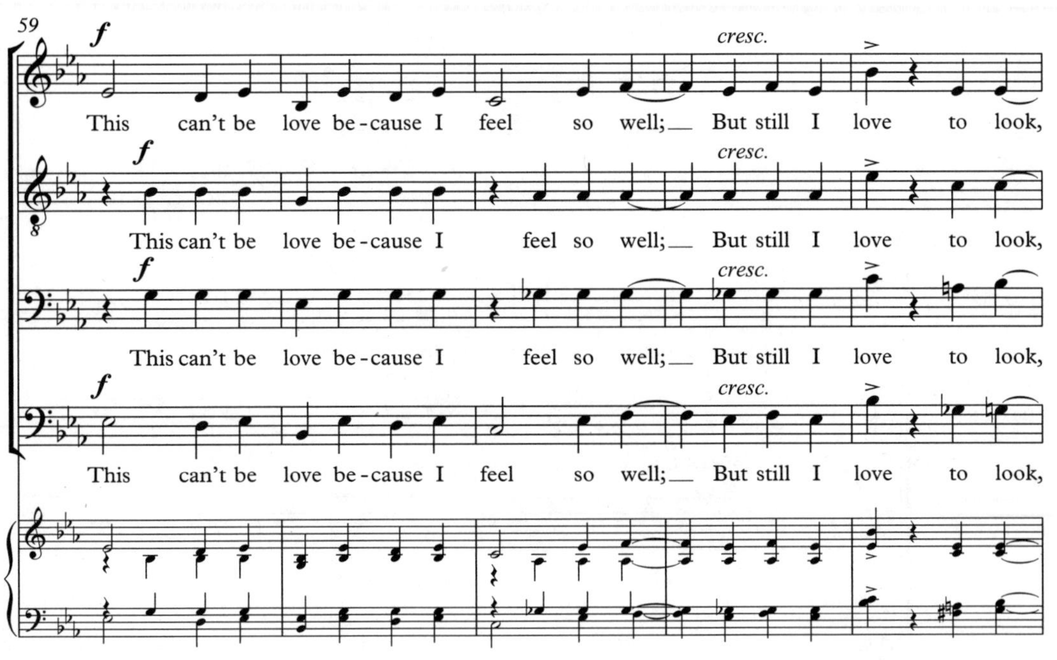

64

rit.

ff

oh yes I love to look oh yes I love to look in your eyes.

ff

oh yes I love to look oh yes I love to look in your eyes.

ff

oh yes I love to look oh yes I love to look in your eyes.

ff

oh yes I love to look oh yes I love to look in your eyes.

rit.

Ain't Misbehavin'

Andy Razaf

Thomas 'Fats' Waller & Harry Brooks
arr. DAVID NIELD

9
ah
hap-py here in-side my cage
ah
ah
hap-py here in-side my cage
ah
hap-py here in-side my cage
ah
Hap-py in-side my cage.
I know who I love best,

13
ah
ah
ah
ah
ah
ah
ah
ah
Thumbs down for all the rest,
My love was giv - en, heart and soul;

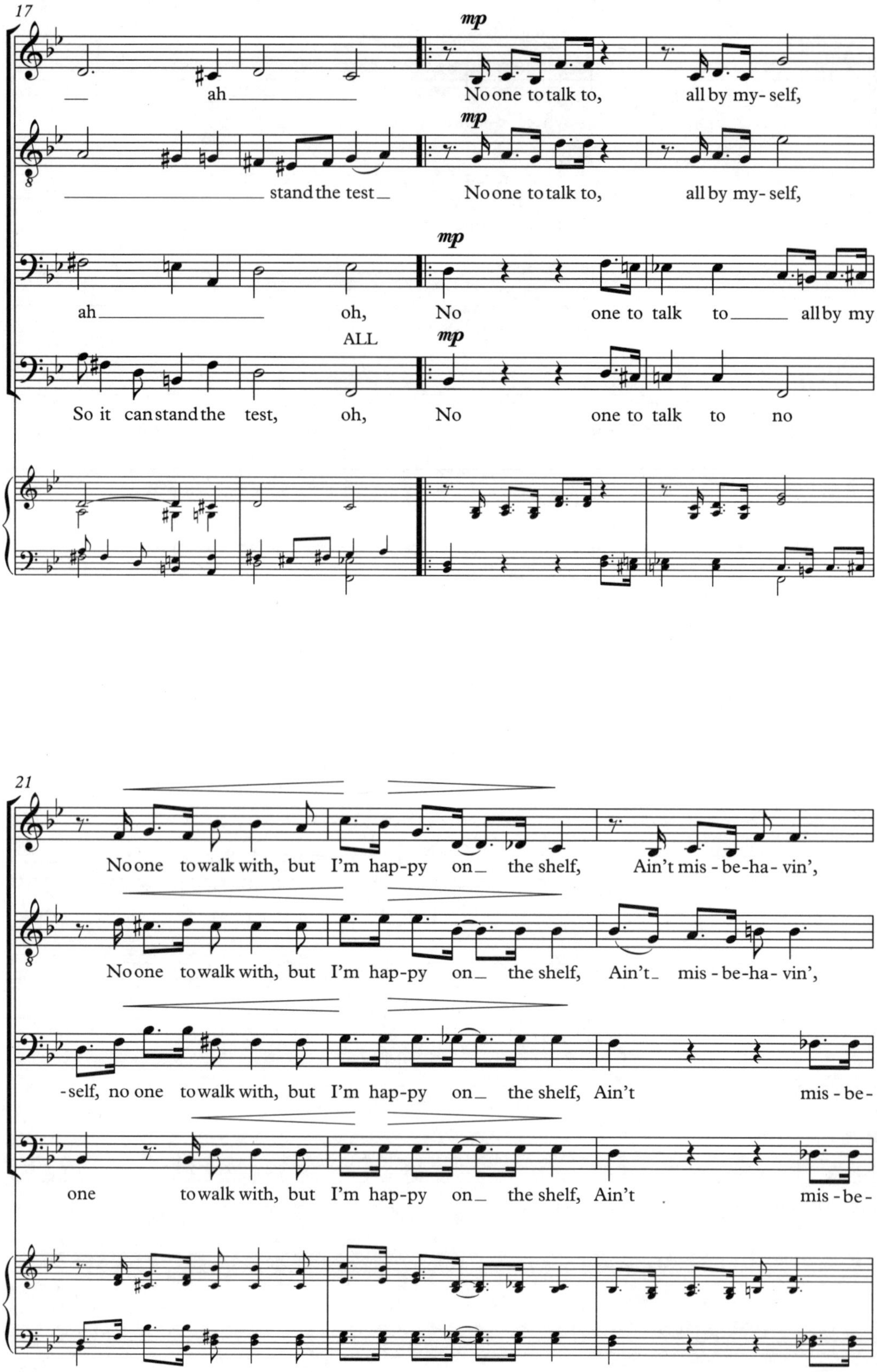

17

mp

— ah ___ No one to talk to, all by my- self,

mp

___ stand the test_ No one to talk to, all by my- self,

mp

ah ___ oh, No one to talk to ___ all by my

ALL mp

So it can stand the test, oh, No one to talk to no

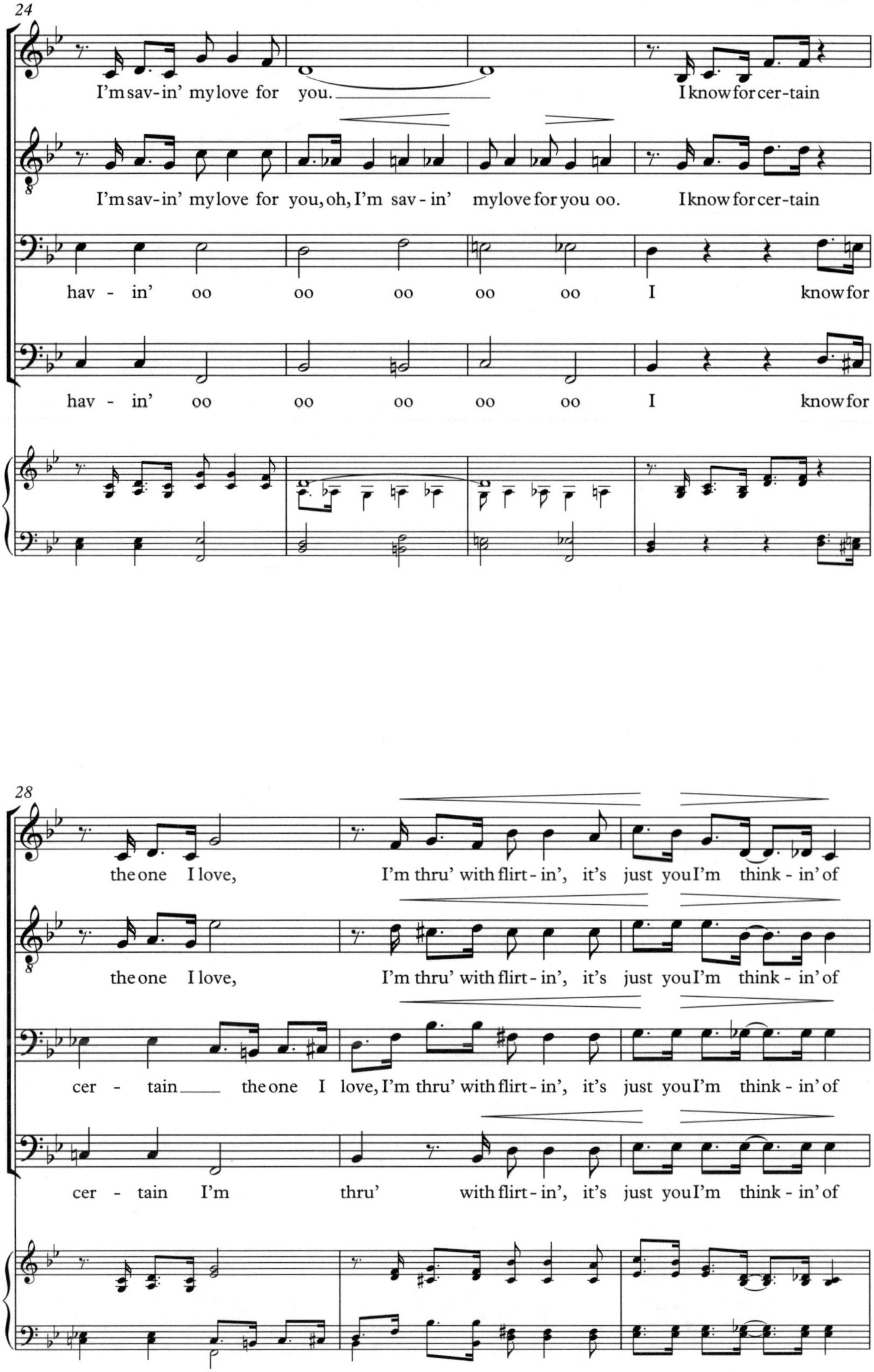

28

the one I love, I'm thru' with flirt - in', it's just you I'm think - in' of

the one I love, I'm thru' with flirt - in', it's just you I'm think - in' of

cer - tain the one I love, I'm thru' with flirt - in', it's just you I'm think - in' of

cer - tain I'm thru' with flirt - in', it's just you I'm think - in' of

31
Ain't mis-be-hav- in', I'm sav- in' my love for you, for you!
Ain't mis-be-hav- in', I'm sav- in' my love for you, love for you, for you!
Ain't mis-be-hav - in' for you, love for you!
Ain't mis-be-hav - in' for you, for you, love for you!

35
f
Like Jack Hor-ner in the cor-ner don't go no-where
Like Jack Hor-ner in the cor-ner don't go no-where
Like Jack Hor - ner in the cor - ner don't go no - where
Like Jack Hor-ner in the cor-ner don't go no-where

38
what do I care, Your kiss-es are worth wait - in' for, be -
what do I care, Your kiss-es are worth wait - in' for, be -
what do I care Your kiss-es are worth wait - in' for be -
what do I care Your kiss-es are worth wait - in' for, be -

42
-lieve me! I don't stay out late don't care to go
-lieve me! I don't stay out late don't care to
-lieve me I don't stay out late don't care to go, I'm
-lieve me I, I don't stay out, don't care, I'm

45
mf
I'm home a-bout eight, just me and my ra - di- o, Ain't mis be-hav - in',
go I'm home at eight, just me and my ra - di- o, Ain't mis be-hav - in', sav-in' my
home at eight just me and my ra - di- o, mis be-hav- in',
f
home at eight just me and my ra - di- o, 'cos I ain't mis be hav - in', I'm

48
SOLO
mf
p
I'm sav- in' my love for you my love for you Your type of man is
love for you, yes I'm sav- in' my love for you oo
I'm sav- in' my love for you, love for you oo
sav- in' my love for you, for you oo

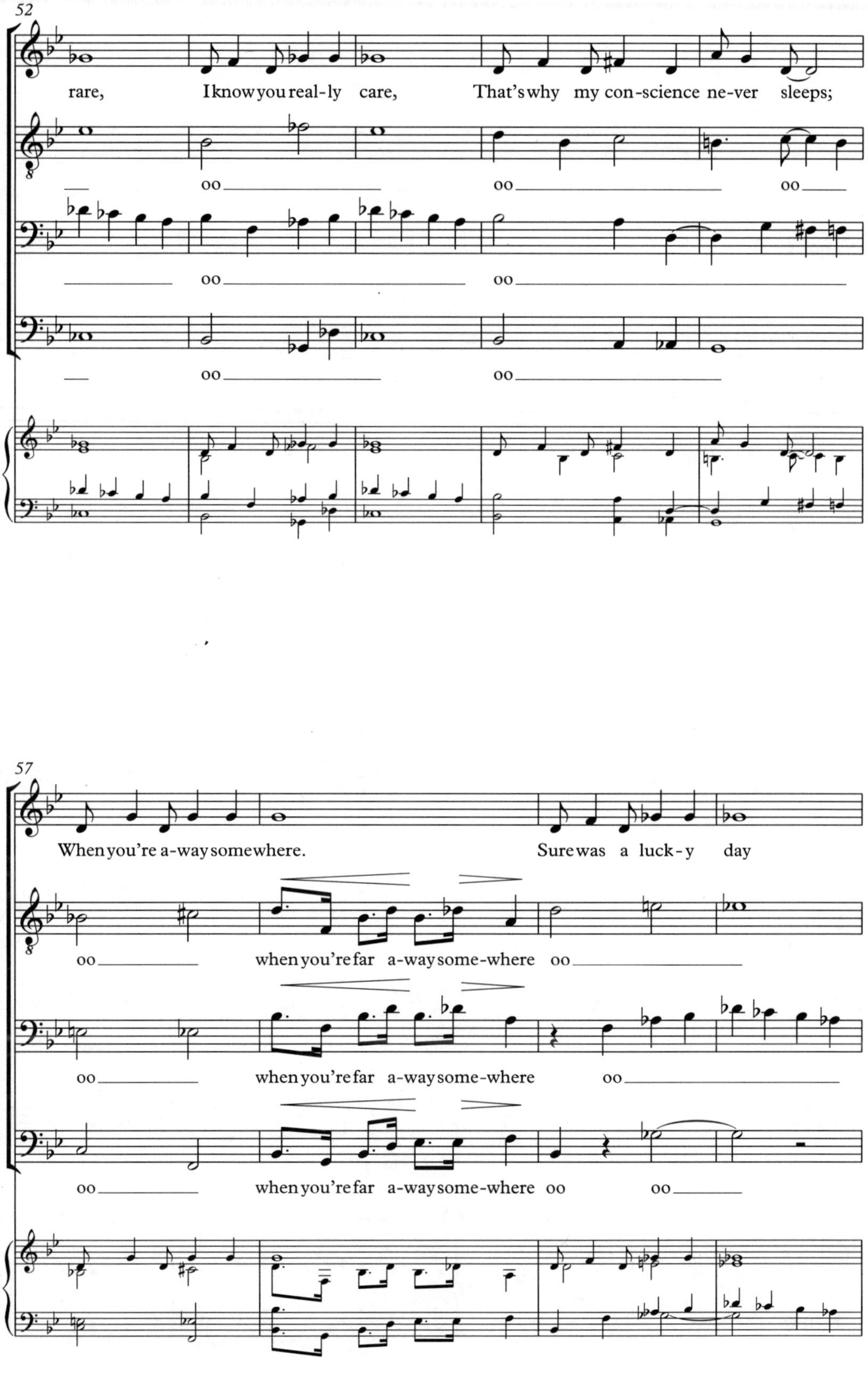

57

When you're a-way some-where. Sure was a luck-y day

oo when you're far a-way some-where oo

oo when you're far a-way some-where oo

oo when you're far a-way some-where oo oo

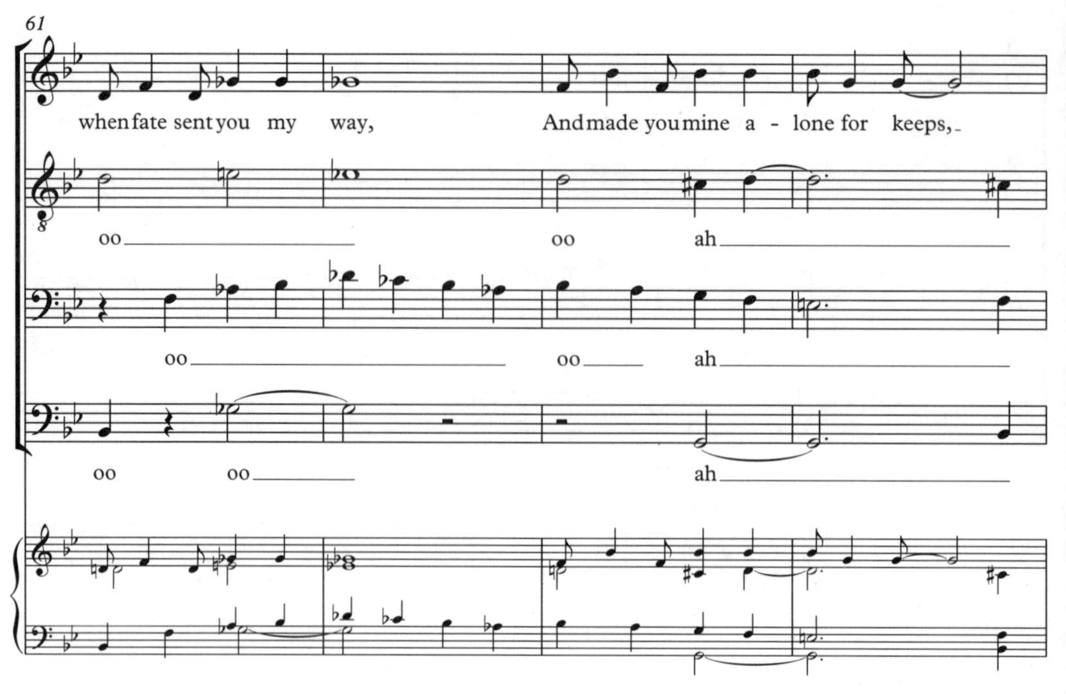

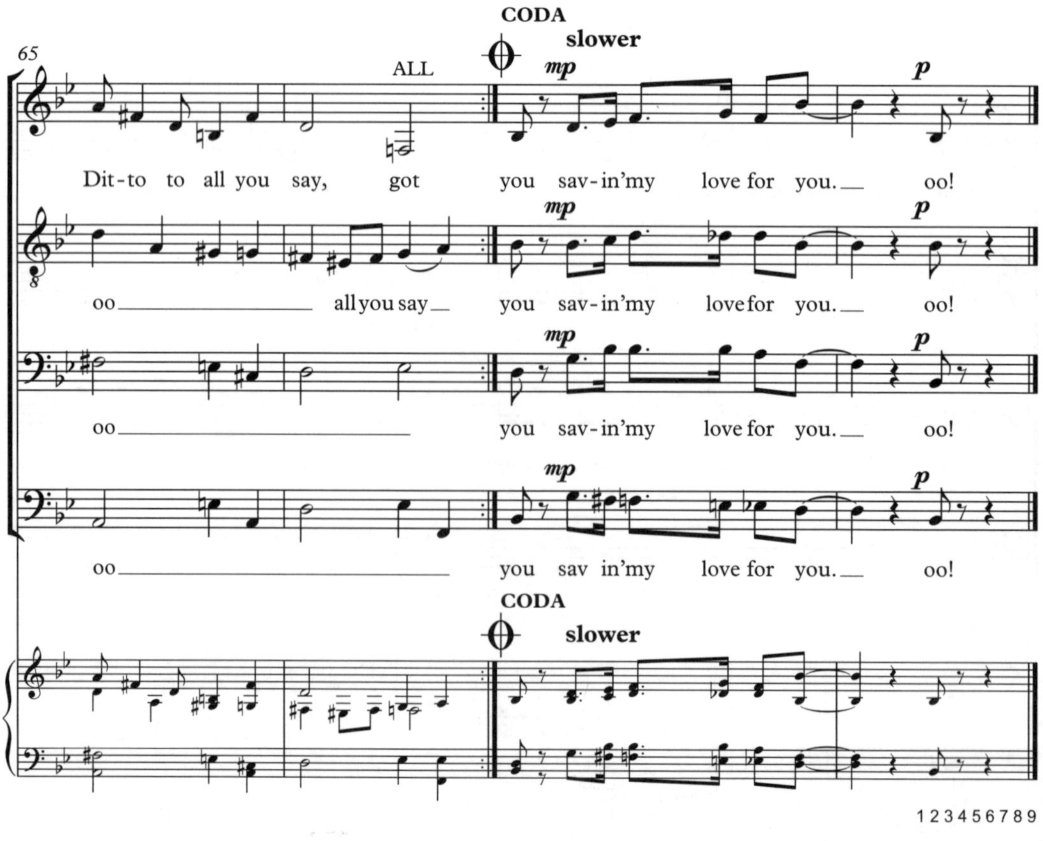

65

CODA

slower

ALL

mp *p*

Dit-to to all you say, got you sav-in'my love for you. oo!

oo all you say you sav-in'my love for you. oo!

oo you sav-in'my love for you. oo!

oo you sav in'my love for you. oo!

CODA

slower

1 2 3 4 5 6 7 8 9